FROM IRELAND'S SHORES
Ireland Address Book

A Collection of Irish Paintings from the Ulster Museum

First published by Appletree Press Ltd, 14 Howard Street South, Belfast BT7 1AP

Copyright © Appletree Press 2004. Text © Appletree Press 2004.

Photographs reproduced with the kind permission of the Trustees of the National Museums and Galleries of Northern Ireland.

FROM IRELAND'S SHORES
Ireland Address Book

A Collection of Irish Paintings from the Ulster Museum

Foreword

This beautiful selection of paintings on the theme of Ireland's shores has been drawn from the Ulster Museum's Fine Art Collections and Armagh County Museum. The Collections – paintings, sculptures, drawings, watercolours and prints – cover a wide spectrum of works, from the 16th century to the present day.

The Friends of the National Collections of Ireland and the Contemporary Art Society have for many years made generous gifts to the Museum. The help of such grant-awarding bodies as The National Art Collections Fund, National Heritage Memorial Fund, the Heritage Lottery Fund and the Esmé Mitchell Trust has been instrumental in enabling the Museum to further enhance its Applied Art holdings. These include significant collections of historic Irish glass and silver, alongside furniture, costume, textiles and jewellery.

The Museum's historical collections of British and Irish watercolours includes extensive holdings by the 19th-century Belfast artists Andrew Nicholl (1804-86) and Dr James Moore (1819-83).

With collections spanning Irish, British, continental European and North American items, the Museum has the most comprehensive assembly of 20th-century art in Ireland.

The Ulster Museum is part of the National Museums and Galleries of Northern Ireland (MAGNI) as is Armagh County Museum.

A

Name: Dr. Philip A. Smyth.
Address: 48 Revelstoke Road,
Southfields
London SW18 5PD
Phone: 02028/9449986 Fax: 02076/309407
Mobile: 07768/076868
E-mail:

Name: Philip / WORK
Address: 260b Fulham Road
Chelsea
SW10 9EL
Phone: 020 73520008 Fax:
Mobile:
E-mail:

Name: Mrs. M. Nabie & Family
Address: 6 Glanleam Drive
Belfast 15
Phone: 90 / ~~340188~~ Fax: 90/371740
Mobile:
E-mail:

Name: ~~Mr + Mrs~~ Mrs Margaret Moore
Address: 59 Castlehill Road,
Belfast
BT4 3GB
Phone: 90/229464 Fax:
Mobile: 07974/562773
E-mail:

Name: Philip
Address:

Phone: 0207~~6~~ Fax:
Mobile: 309 407
E-mail:

Name:
Address:

Phone: Fax:
Mobile:
E-mail:

Landscape near Falcarragh, Co. Donegal *Watercolour, bodycolour on paper 18 x 25 cm* **Percy French** *(1854-1920)*

A

Name: MR. K. Mc Williams
Address: 2 Royal Oaks,
Belfast
BT8 4YX

Phone: Fax:

Mobile:

E-mail:

Name:

Address:

Phone: Fax:

Mobile:

E-mail:

Name:

Address:

Phone: Fax:

Mobile:

E-mail:

Name:

Address:

Phone: Fax:

Mobile:

E-mail:

Name:

Address:

Phone: Fax:

Mobile:

E-mail:

Name:

Address:

Phone: Fax:

Mobile:

E-mail:

Name:

Address:

Phone: Fax:

Mobile:

E-mail:

Name:

Address:

Phone: Fax:

Mobile:

E-mail:

Name:

Address:

Phone: Fax:

Mobile:

E-mail:

Name:

Address:

Phone: Fax:

Mobile:

E-mail:

Name:

Address:

Phone: Fax:

Mobile:

E-mail:

Name:

Address:

Phone: Fax:

Mobile:

E-mail:

B

Name:

Address:

Phone: Fax:

Mobile:

E-mail:

Name:

Address:

Phone: Fax:

Mobile:

E-mail:

Name:

Address:

Phone: Fax:

Mobile:

E-mail:

Name:

Address:

Phone: Fax:

Mobile:

E-mail:

Name:

Address:

Phone: Fax:

Mobile:

E-mail:

Name:

Address:

Phone: Fax:

Mobile:

E-mail:

Dunluce Castle *Pencil, watercolour, white on paper 50.4 x 74.4 cm* **Andrew Nicholl** *(1804-1886)*

B

Name:

Address:

Phone: Fax:

Mobile:

E-mail:

Name:

Address:

Phone: Fax:

Mobile:

E-mail:

Name:

Address:

Phone: Fax:

Mobile:

E-mail:

Name:

Address:

Phone: Fax:

Mobile:

E-mail:

Name:

Address:

Phone: Fax:

Mobile:

E-mail:

Name:

Address:

Phone: Fax:

Mobile:

E-mail:

Name:

Address:

Phone: Fax:

Mobile:

E-mail:

Name:

Address:

Phone: Fax:

Mobile:

E-mail:

Name:

Address:

Phone: Fax:

Mobile:

E-mail:

Name:

Address:

Phone: Fax:

Mobile:

E-mail:

Name:

Address:

Phone: Fax:

Mobile:

E-mail:

Name:

Address:

Phone: Fax:

Mobile:

E-mail:

C

Name:

Address:

Phone: Fax:

Mobile:

E-mail:

Name:

Address:

Phone: Fax:

Mobile:

E-mail:

Name:

Address:

Phone: Fax:

Mobile:

E-mail:

Name:

Address:

Phone: Fax:

Mobile:

E-mail:

Name:

Address:

Phone: Fax:

Mobile:

E-mail:

Name:

Address:

Phone: Fax:

Mobile:

E-mail:

Lake of Killarney, Co. Kerry (1815) *Pencil, ink, watercolour on paper 38 x 48.3 cm* **John Henry Campbell** *(1757-1828)*

C

Name:

Address:

Phone: Fax:

Mobile:

E-mail:

Name:

Address:

Phone: Fax:

Mobile:

E-mail:

Name:

Address:

Phone: Fax:

Mobile:

E-mail:

Name:

Address:

Phone: Fax:

Mobile:

E-mail:

Name:

Address:

Phone: Fax:

Mobile:

E-mail:

Name:

Address:

Phone: Fax:

Mobile:

E-mail:

Name:

Address:

Phone: Fax:

Mobile:

E-mail:

Name:

Address:

Phone: Fax:

Mobile:

E-mail:

Name:

Address:

Phone: Fax:

Mobile:

E-mail:

Name:

Address:

Phone: Fax:

Mobile:

E-mail:

Name:

Address:

Phone: Fax:

Mobile:

E-mail:

Name:

Address:

Phone: Fax:

Mobile:

E-mail:

D

Name:

Address:

Phone: Fax:

Mobile:

E-mail:

Name:

Address:

Phone: Fax:

Mobile:

E-mail:

Name:

Address:

Phone: Fax:

Mobile:

E-mail:

Name:

Address:

Phone: Fax:

Mobile:

E-mail:

Name:

Address:

Phone: Fax:

Mobile:

E-mail:

Name:

Address:

Phone: Fax:

Mobile:

E-mail:

Evening   *Watercolour, white on paper 36.7 x 54 cm*   **Helen O'Hara** *(1846-1920)*

D

Name:

Address:

Phone: Fax:

Mobile:

E-mail:

Name:

Address:

Phone: Fax:

Mobile:

E-mail:

Name:

Address:

Phone: Fax:

Mobile:

E-mail:

Name:

Address:

Phone: Fax:

Mobile:

E-mail:

Name:

Address:

Phone: Fax:

Mobile:

E-mail:

Name:

Address:

Phone: Fax:

Mobile:

E-mail:

Name:

Address:

Phone: Fax:

Mobile:

E-mail:

Name:

Address:

Phone: Fax:

Mobile:

E-mail:

Name:

Address:

Phone: Fax:

Mobile:

E-mail:

Name:

Address:

Phone: Fax:

Mobile:

E-mail:

Name:

Address:

Phone: Fax:

Mobile:

E-mail:

Name:

Address:

Phone: Fax:

Mobile:

E-mail:

E

Name:

Address:

Phone: Fax:

Mobile:

E-mail:

Name:

Address:

Phone: Fax:

Mobile:

E-mail:

Name:

Address:

Phone: Fax:

Mobile:

E-mail:

Name:

Address:

Phone: Fax:

Mobile:

E-mail:

Name:

Address:

Phone: Fax:

Mobile:

E-mail:

Name:

Address:

Phone: Fax:

Mobile:

E-mail:

Looking from Ardsbeg, Co. Donegal (1921) *Pencil, watercolour on paper 37.5 x 53 cm* **John Alphonsus McAllister** (1896-1925)

E

Name:

Address:

Phone: Fax:

Mobile:

E-mail:

Name:

Address:

Phone: Fax:

Mobile:

E-mail:

Name:

Address:

Phone: Fax:

Mobile:

E-mail:

Name:

Address:

Phone: Fax:

Mobile:

E-mail:

Name:

Address:

Phone: Fax:

Mobile:

E-mail:

Name:

Address:

Phone: Fax:

Mobile:

E-mail:

Name:

Address:

Phone: Fax:

Mobile:

E-mail:

Name:

Address:

Phone: Fax:

Mobile:

E-mail:

Name:

Address:

Phone: Fax:

Mobile:

E-mail:

Name:

Address:

Phone: Fax:

Mobile:

E-mail:

Name:

Address:

Phone: Fax:

Mobile:

E-mail:

Name:

Address:

Phone: Fax:

Mobile:

E-mail:

F

Name:

Address:

Phone: Fax:

Mobile:

E-mail:

Name:

Address:

Phone: Fax:

Mobile:

E-mail:

Name:

Address:

Phone: Fax:

Mobile:

E-mail:

Name:

Address:

Phone: Fax:

Mobile:

E-mail:

Name:

Address:

Phone: Fax:

Mobile:

E-mail:

Name:

Address:

Phone: Fax:

Mobile:

E-mail:

The Fairies' Lough   *Watercolour on paper 13 x 17.5 cm*   **Percy French** *(1854-1920)*

F

Name:

Address:

Phone: Fax:

Mobile:

E-mail:

Name:

Address:

Phone: Fax:

Mobile:

E-mail:

Name:

Address:

Phone: Fax:

Mobile:

E-mail:

Name:

Address:

Phone: Fax:

Mobile:

E-mail:

Name:

Address:

Phone: Fax:

Mobile:

E-mail:

Name:

Address:

Phone: Fax:

Mobile:

E-mail:

Name:

Address:

Phone: Fax:

Mobile:

E-mail:

Name:

Address:

Phone: Fax:

Mobile:

E-mail:

Name:

Address:

Phone: Fax:

Mobile:

E-mail:

Name:

Address:

Phone: Fax:

Mobile:

E-mail:

Name:

Address:

Phone: Fax:

Mobile:

E-mail:

Name:

Address:

Phone: Fax:

Mobile:

E-mail:

G

Name:	Name:
Address:	Address:
Phone: Fax:	Phone: Fax:
Mobile:	Mobile:
E-mail:	E-mail:
Name:	Name:
Address:	Address:
Phone: Fax:	Phone: Fax:
Mobile:	Mobile:
E-mail:	E-mail:
Name:	Name:
Address:	Address:
Phone: Fax:	Phone: Fax:
Mobile:	Mobile:
E-mail:	E-mail:

View of Bangor Bay from the Harbour *Watercolour on paper 17.2 x 24.6 cm* **Miss Lawson** *(19th century)*

G

Name:

Address:

Phone: Fax:

Mobile:

E-mail:

Name:

Address:

Phone: Fax:

Mobile:

E-mail:

Name:

Address:

Phone: Fax:

Mobile:

E-mail:

Name:

Address:

Phone: Fax:

Mobile:

E-mail:

Name:

Address:

Phone: Fax:

Mobile:

E-mail:

Name:

Address:

Phone: Fax:

Mobile:

E-mail:

Name:

Address:

Phone: Fax:

Mobile:

E-mail:

Name:

Address:

Phone: Fax:

Mobile:

E-mail:

Name:

Address:

Phone: Fax:

Mobile:

E-mail:

Name:

Address:

Phone: Fax:

Mobile:

E-mail:

Name:

Address:

Phone: Fax:

Mobile:

E-mail:

Name:

Address:

Phone: Fax:

Mobile:

E-mail:

H

Name:

Address:

Phone: Fax:

Mobile:

E-mail:

Name:

Address:

Phone: Fax:

Mobile:

E-mail:

Name:

Address:

Phone: Fax:

Mobile:

E-mail:

Name:

Address:

Phone: Fax:

Mobile:

E-mail:

Name:

Address:

Phone: Fax:

Mobile:

E-mail:

Name:

Address:

Phone: Fax:

Mobile:

E-mail:

Carriganass Castle, Co. Cork   *Watercolour on paper 63.5 x 97 cm*   **Henry Albert Hartland** *(1840-1893)*

H

Name:

Address:

Phone: Fax:

Mobile:

E-mail:

Name:

Address:

Phone: Fax:

Mobile:

E-mail:

Name:

Address:

Phone: Fax:

Mobile:

E-mail:

Name:

Address:

Phone: Fax:

Mobile:

E-mail:

Name:

Address:

Phone: Fax:

Mobile:

E-mail:

Name:

Address:

Phone: Fax:

Mobile:

E-mail:

Name:		Name:	
Address:		Address:	
Phone:	Fax:	Phone:	Fax:
Mobile:		Mobile:	
E-mail:		E-mail:	

Name:		Name:	
Address:		Address:	
Phone:	Fax:	Phone:	Fax:
Mobile:		Mobile:	
E-mail:		E-mail:	

Name:		Name:	
Address:		Address:	
Phone:	Fax:	Phone:	Fax:
Mobile:		Mobile:	
E-mail:		E-mail:	

Name:

Address:

Phone: Fax:

Mobile:

E-mail:

Name:

Address:

Phone: Fax:

Mobile:

E-mail:

Name:

Address:

Phone: Fax:

Mobile:

E-mail:

Name:

Address:

Phone: Fax:

Mobile:

E-mail:

Name:

Address:

Phone: Fax:

Mobile:

E-mail:

Name:

Address:

Phone: Fax:

Mobile:

E-mail:

Pigeon Cave and Dunree Fort, Lough Swilly *Watercolour on paper 35 x 49 cm (sight)* **Andrew Nicholl** *(1804-1886)*

Name:	Name:
Address:	Address:
Phone: Fax:	Phone: Fax:
Mobile:	Mobile:
E-mail:	E-mail:
Name:	Name:
Address:	Address:
Phone: Fax:	Phone: Fax:
Mobile:	Mobile:
E-mail:	E-mail:
Name:	Name:
Address:	Address:
Phone: Fax:	Phone: Fax:
Mobile:	Mobile:
E-mail:	E-mail:

Name:

Address:

Phone: Fax:

Mobile:

E-mail:

Name:

Address:

Phone: Fax:

Mobile:

E-mail:

Name:

Address:

Phone: Fax:

Mobile:

E-mail:

Name:

Address:

Phone: Fax:

Mobile:

E-mail:

Name:

Address:

Phone: Fax:

Mobile:

E-mail:

Name:

Address:

Phone: Fax:

Mobile:

E-mail:

J

Name:

Address:

Phone: Fax:

Mobile:

E-mail:

Name:

Address:

Phone: Fax:

Mobile:

E-mail:

Name:

Address:

Phone: Fax:

Mobile:

E-mail:

Name:

Address:

Phone: Fax:

Mobile:

E-mail:

Name:

Address:

Phone: Fax:

Mobile:

E-mail:

Name:

Address:

Phone: Fax:

Mobile:

E-mail:

The End of the Fair, Back to the Island (1910) *Oil on canvas 35.6 x 55.8 cm* **William Henry Bartlett** *(1858-1932)*

J

Name:

Address:

Phone: Fax:

Mobile:

E-mail:

Name:

Address:

Phone: Fax:

Mobile:

E-mail:

Name:

Address:

Phone: Fax:

Mobile:

E-mail:

Name:

Address:

Phone: Fax:

Mobile:

E-mail:

Name:

Address:

Phone: Fax:

Mobile:

E-mail:

Name:

Address:

Phone: Fax:

Mobile:

E-mail:

Name:

Address:

Phone: Fax:

Mobile:

E-mail:

Name:

Address:

Phone: Fax:

Mobile:

E-mail:

Name:

Address:

Phone: Fax:

Mobile:

E-mail:

Name:

Address:

Phone: Fax:

Mobile:

E-mail:

Name:

Address:

Phone: Fax:

Mobile:

E-mail:

Name:

Address:

Phone: Fax:

Mobile:

E-mail:

K

Name:

Address:

Phone: Fax:

Mobile:

E-mail:

Name:

Address:

Phone: Fax:

Mobile:

E-mail:

Name:

Address:

Phone: Fax:

Mobile:

E-mail:

Name:

Address:

Phone: Fax:

Mobile:

E-mail:

Name:

Address:

Phone: Fax:

Mobile:

E-mail:

Name:

Address:

Phone: Fax:

Mobile:

E-mail:

Bundoran Sands: Stormy Day *Oil on board 17.9 x 26.6 cm* **Nathaniel Hone** *(1831-1917)*

K

Name:

Address:

Phone: Fax:

Mobile:

E-mail:

Name:

Address:

Phone: Fax:

Mobile:

E-mail:

Name:

Address:

Phone: Fax:

Mobile:

E-mail:

Name:

Address:

Phone: Fax:

Mobile:

E-mail:

Name:

Address:

Phone: Fax:

Mobile:

E-mail:

Name:

Address:

Phone: Fax:

Mobile:

E-mail:

Name:

Address:

Phone: Fax:

Mobile:

E-mail:

Name:

Address:

Phone: Fax:

Mobile:

E-mail:

Name:

Address:

Phone: Fax:

Mobile:

E-mail:

Name:

Address:

Phone: Fax:

Mobile:

E-mail:

Name:

Address:

Phone: Fax:

Mobile:

E-mail:

Name:

Address:

Phone: Fax:

Mobile:

E-mail:

L

Name:

Address:

Phone: Fax:

Mobile:

E-mail:

Name:

Address:

Phone: Fax:

Mobile:

E-mail:

Name:

Address:

Phone: Fax:

Mobile:

E-mail:

Name:

Address:

Phone: Fax:

Mobile:

E-mail:

Name:

Address:

Phone: Fax:

Mobile:

E-mail:

Name:

Address:

Phone: Fax:

Mobile:

E-mail:

Five Trees by a River   *Oil on canvas on panel 15.3 x 24.7 cm*   **Hans Iten** *(1874-1930)*

L

Name:

Address:

Phone: Fax:

Mobile:

E-mail:

Name:

Address:

Phone: Fax:

Mobile:

E-mail:

Name:

Address:

Phone: Fax:

Mobile:

E-mail:

Name:

Address:

Phone: Fax:

Mobile:

E-mail:

Name:

Address:

Phone: Fax:

Mobile:

E-mail:

Name:

Address:

Phone: Fax:

Mobile:

E-mail:

Name:

Address:

Phone: Fax:

Mobile:

E-mail:

Name:

Address:

Phone: Fax:

Mobile:

E-mail:

Name:

Address:

Phone: Fax:

Mobile:

E-mail:

Name:

Address:

Phone: Fax:

Mobile:

E-mail:

Name:

Address:

Phone: Fax:

Mobile:

E-mail:

Name:

Address:

Phone: Fax:

Mobile:

E-mail:

M

Name:

Address:

Phone: Fax:

Mobile:

E-mail:

Name:

Address:

Phone: Fax:

Mobile:

E-mail:

Name:

Address:

Phone: Fax:

Mobile:

E-mail:

Name:

Address:

Phone: Fax:

Mobile:

E-mail:

Name:

Address:

Phone: Fax:

Mobile:

E-mail:

Name:

Address:

Phone: Fax:

Mobile:

E-mail:

Sandy Bay *Pencil, watercolour, white on paper 15.9 x 23.8 cm* **Arthur Gilmer** *(1882-1929)*

Name:

Address:

Phone: Fax:

Mobile:

E-mail:

Name:

Address:

Phone: Fax:

Mobile:

E-mail:

Name:

Address:

Phone: Fax:

Mobile:

E-mail:

Name:

Address:

Phone: Fax:

Mobile:

E-mail:

Name:

Address:

Phone: Fax:

Mobile:

E-mail:

Name:

Address:

Phone: Fax:

Mobile:

E-mail:

Name:

Address:

Phone: Fax:

Mobile:

E-mail:

Name:

Address:

Phone: Fax:

Mobile:

E-mail:

Name:

Address:

Phone: Fax:

Mobile:

E-mail:

Name:

Address:

Phone: Fax:

Mobile:

E-mail:

Name:

Address:

Phone: Fax:

Mobile:

E-mail:

Name:

Address:

Phone: Fax:

Mobile:

E-mail:

Mc

Name:	Name:
Address:	Address:
Phone: Fax:	Phone: Fax:
Mobile:	Mobile:
E-mail:	E-mail:
Name:	Name:
Address:	Address:
Phone: Fax:	Phone: Fax:
Mobile:	Mobile:
E-mail:	E-mail:
Name:	Name:
Address:	Address:
Phone: Fax:	Phone: Fax:
Mobile:	Mobile:
E-mail:	E-mail:

Ringsend from Beggar's Bush, Co. Dublin   *Watercolour on paper 20.8 x 30.5 cm*   **Francis Danby** *(1793-1861)*

Mc

Name:

Address:

Phone: Fax:

Mobile:

E-mail:

Name:

Address:

Phone: Fax:

Mobile:

E-mail:

Name:

Address:

Phone: Fax:

Mobile:

E-mail:

Name:

Address:

Phone: Fax:

Mobile:

E-mail:

Name:

Address:

Phone: Fax:

Mobile:

E-mail:

Name:

Address:

Phone: Fax:

Mobile:

E-mail:

Name:

Address:

Phone: Fax:

Mobile:

E-mail:

Name:

Address:

Phone: Fax:

Mobile:

E-mail:

Name:

Address:

Phone: Fax:

Mobile:

E-mail:

Name:

Address:

Phone: Fax:

Mobile:

E-mail:

Name:

Address:

Phone: Fax:

Mobile:

E-mail:

Name:

Address:

Phone: Fax:

Mobile:

E-mail:

N

Name:

Address:

Phone: Fax:

Mobile:

E-mail:

Name:

Address:

Phone: Fax:

Mobile:

E-mail:

Name:

Address:

Phone: Fax:

Mobile:

E-mail:

Name:

Address:

Phone: Fax:

Mobile:

E-mail:

Name:

Address:

Phone: Fax:

Mobile:

E-mail:

Name:

Address:

Phone: Fax:

Mobile:

E-mail:

Corner of the Lake *Watercolour, pencil, gouache on paper 24.3 x 35.4 cm* **William Mark Fisher** *(1841-1923)*

N

Name:	Name:
Address:	Address:
Phone: Fax:	Phone: Fax:
Mobile:	Mobile:
E-mail:	E-mail:
Name:	Name:
Address:	Address:
Phone: Fax:	Phone: Fax:
Mobile:	Mobile:
E-mail:	E-mail:
Name:	Name:
Address:	Address:
Phone: Fax:	Phone: Fax:
Mobile:	Mobile:
E-mail:	E-mail:

Name:

Address:

Phone: Fax:

Mobile:

E-mail:

Name:

Address:

Phone: Fax:

Mobile:

E-mail:

Name:

Address:

Phone: Fax:

Mobile:

E-mail:

Name:

Address:

Phone: Fax:

Mobile:

E-mail:

Name:

Address:

Phone: Fax:

Mobile:

E-mail:

Name:

Address:

Phone: Fax:

Mobile:

E-mail:

Name:

Address:

Phone: Fax:

Mobile:

E-mail:

Name:

Address:

Phone: Fax:

Mobile:

E-mail:

Name:

Address:

Phone: Fax:

Mobile:

E-mail:

Name:

Address:

Phone: Fax:

Mobile:

E-mail:

Name:

Address:

Phone: Fax:

Mobile:

E-mail:

Name:

Address:

Phone: Fax:

Mobile:

E-mail:

West Prospect of the Giant's Causeway (c.1739)   *Gouache on vellum 34.1 x 66.6 cm*   **Susanna Drury** *(fl.1733-1770)*

Name:

Address:

Phone: Fax:

Mobile:

E-mail:

Name:

Address:

Phone: Fax:

Mobile:

E-mail:

Name:

Address:

Phone: Fax:

Mobile:

E-mail:

Name:

Address:

Phone: Fax:

Mobile:

E-mail:

Name:

Address:

Phone: Fax:

Mobile:

E-mail:

Name:

Address:

Phone: Fax:

Mobile:

E-mail:

Name:

Address:

Phone: Fax:

Mobile:

E-mail:

Name:

Address:

Phone: Fax:

Mobile:

E-mail:

Name:

Address:

Phone: Fax:

Mobile:

E-mail:

Name:

Address:

Phone: Fax:

Mobile:

E-mail:

Name:

Address:

Phone: Fax:

Mobile:

E-mail:

Name:

Address:

Phone: Fax:

Mobile:

E-mail:

P

Name:
Address:

Phone: Fax:
Mobile:
E-mail:

Name:
Address:

Phone: Fax:
Mobile:
E-mail:

Name:
Address:

Phone: Fax:
Mobile:
E-mail:

Name:
Address:

Phone: Fax:
Mobile:
E-mail:

Name:
Address:

Phone: Fax:
Mobile:
E-mail:

Name:
Address:

Phone: Fax:
Mobile:
E-mail:

The Eagle's Nest, Killarney   *Oil on panel 48.5 x 80 cm*   **William II Sadler** *(1782-1839)*

P

Name:

Address:

Phone: Fax:

Mobile:

E-mail:

Name:

Address:

Phone: Fax:

Mobile:

E-mail:

Name:

Address:

Phone: Fax:

Mobile:

E-mail:

Name:

Address:

Phone: Fax:

Mobile:

E-mail:

Name:

Address:

Phone: Fax:

Mobile:

E-mail:

Name:

Address:

Phone: Fax:

Mobile:

E-mail:

Name:

Address:

Phone: Fax:

Mobile:

E-mail:

Name:

Address:

Phone: Fax:

Mobile:

E-mail:

Name:

Address:

Phone: Fax:

Mobile:

E-mail:

Name:

Address:

Phone: Fax:

Mobile:

E-mail:

Name:

Address:

Phone: Fax:

Mobile:

E-mail:

Name:

Address:

Phone: Fax:

Mobile:

E-mail:

Q

Name:

Address:

Phone: Fax:

Mobile:

E-mail:

Name:

Address:

Phone: Fax:

Mobile:

E-mail:

Name:

Address:

Phone: Fax:

Mobile:

E-mail:

Name:

Address:

Phone: Fax:

Mobile:

E-mail:

Name:

Address:

Phone: Fax:

Mobile:

E-mail:

Name:

Address:

Phone: Fax:

Mobile:

E-mail:

Surge of the Sea, Ardglass   *Oil on board 26.9 x 34.8 cm*   **Hans Iten** *(1874-1930)*

Q

Name:

Address:

Phone: Fax:

Mobile:

E-mail:

Name:

Address:

Phone: Fax:

Mobile:

E-mail:

Name:

Address:

Phone: Fax:

Mobile:

E-mail:

Name:

Address:

Phone: Fax:

Mobile:

E-mail:

Name:

Address:

Phone: Fax:

Mobile:

E-mail:

Name:

Address:

Phone: Fax:

Mobile:

E-mail:

Name:		Name:	
Address:		Address:	
Phone:	Fax:	Phone:	Fax:
Mobile:		Mobile:	
E-mail:		E-mail:	

Name:		Name:	
Address:		Address:	
Phone:	Fax:	Phone:	Fax:
Mobile:		Mobile:	
E-mail:		E-mail:	

Name:		Name:	
Address:		Address:	
Phone:	Fax:	Phone:	Fax:
Mobile:		Mobile:	
E-mail:		E-mail:	

R

Name:

Address:

Phone: Fax:

Mobile:

E-mail:

Name:

Address:

Phone: Fax:

Mobile:

E-mail:

Name:

Address:

Phone: Fax:

Mobile:

E-mail:

Name:

Address:

Phone: Fax:

Mobile:

E-mail:

Name:

Address:

Phone: Fax:

Mobile:

E-mail:

Name:

Address:

Phone: Fax:

Mobile:

E-mail:

Scene in Co. Wicklow (1820) *Oil on canvas 70.8 x 91.3 cm* **James Arthur O'Connor** *(1792-1841)*

R

Name:

Address:

Phone: **Fax:**

Mobile:

E-mail:

Name:

Address:

Phone: **Fax:**

Mobile:

E-mail:

Name:

Address:

Phone: **Fax:**

Mobile:

E-mail:

Name:

Address:

Phone: **Fax:**

Mobile:

E-mail:

Name:

Address:

Phone: **Fax:**

Mobile:

E-mail:

Name:

Address:

Phone: **Fax:**

Mobile:

E-mail:

Name:

Address:

Phone: Fax:

Mobile:

E-mail:

Name:

Address:

Phone: Fax:

Mobile:

E-mail:

Name:

Address:

Phone: Fax:

Mobile:

E-mail:

Name:

Address:

Phone: Fax:

Mobile:

E-mail:

Name:

Address:

Phone: Fax:

Mobile:

E-mail:

Name:

Address:

Phone: Fax:

Mobile:

E-mail:

S

Name:

Address:

Phone: Fax:

Mobile:

E-mail:

Name:

Address:

Phone: Fax:

Mobile:

E-mail:

Name:

Address:

Phone: Fax:

Mobile:

E-mail:

Name:

Address:

Phone: Fax:

Mobile:

E-mail:

Name:

Address:

Phone: Fax:

Mobile:

E-mail:

Name:

Address:

Phone: Fax:

Mobile:

E-mail:

On the Quay, Belfast (1889) *Ink on board 24.5 x 34.8 cm* **John Percival Gülich** (1864-1898)

S

Name:

Address:

Phone: Fax:

Mobile:

E-mail:

Name:

Address:

Phone: Fax:

Mobile:

E-mail:

Name:

Address:

Phone: Fax:

Mobile:

E-mail:

Name:

Address:

Phone: Fax:

Mobile:

E-mail:

Name:

Address:

Phone: Fax:

Mobile:

E-mail:

Name:

Address:

Phone: Fax:

Mobile:

E-mail:

Name:

Address:

Phone: Fax:

Mobile:

E-mail:

Name:

Address:

Phone: Fax:

Mobile:

E-mail:

Name:

Address:

Phone: Fax:

Mobile:

E-mail:

Name:

Address:

Phone: Fax:

Mobile:

E-mail:

Name:

Address:

Phone: Fax:

Mobile:

E-mail:

Name:

Address:

Phone: Fax:

Mobile:

E-mail:

S

Name:

Address:

Phone: Fax:

Mobile:

E-mail:

Name:

Address:

Phone: Fax:

Mobile:

E-mail:

Name:

Address:

Phone: Fax:

Mobile:

E-mail:

Name:

Address:

Phone: Fax:

Mobile:

E-mail:

Name:

Address:

Phone: Fax:

Mobile:

E-mail:

Name:

Address:

Phone: Fax:

Mobile:

E-mail:

Attack of the French Squadron... upon the Coast of Ireland (1799) *Oil on cavas 69.4 x 99.5 cm* **Nicholas Pocock** *(1740-1821)*

S

Name:

Address:

Phone: Fax:

Mobile:

E-mail:

Name:

Address:

Phone: Fax:

Mobile:

E-mail:

Name:

Address:

Phone: Fax:

Mobile:

E-mail:

Name:

Address:

Phone: Fax:

Mobile:

E-mail:

Name:

Address:

Phone: Fax:

Mobile:

E-mail:

Name:

Address:

Phone: Fax:

Mobile:

E-mail:

Name:

Address:

Phone: Fax:

Mobile:

E-mail:

Name:

Address:

Phone: Fax:

Mobile:

E-mail:

Name:

Address:

Phone: Fax:

Mobile:

E-mail:

Name:

Address:

Phone: Fax:

Mobile:

E-mail:

Name:

Address:

Phone: Fax:

Mobile:

E-mail:

Name:

Address:

Phone: Fax:

Mobile:

E-mail:

T

Name:

Address:

Phone: Fax:

Mobile:

E-mail:

Name:

Address:

Phone: Fax:

Mobile:

E-mail:

Name:

Address:

Phone: Fax:

Mobile:

E-mail:

Name:

Address:

Phone: Fax:

Mobile:

E-mail:

Name:

Address:

Phone: Fax:

Mobile:

E-mail:

Name:

Address:

Phone: Fax:

Mobile:

E-mail:

Waterfoot Harbour, Co. Antrim (1924) *Pencil, watercolour on paper 28.6 x 39.8 cm* **John Alphonsus McAllister** *(1896-1925)*

T

Name:

Address:

Phone: Fax:

Mobile:

E-mail:

Name:

Address:

Phone: Fax:

Mobile:

E-mail:

Name:

Address:

Phone: Fax:

Mobile:

E-mail:

Name:

Address:

Phone: Fax:

Mobile:

E-mail:

Name:

Address:

Phone: Fax:

Mobile:

E-mail:

Name:

Address:

Phone: Fax:

Mobile:

E-mail:

Name:

Address:

Phone: Fax:

Mobile:

E-mail:

Name:

Address:

Phone: Fax:

Mobile:

E-mail:

Name:

Address:

Phone: Fax:

Mobile:

E-mail:

Name:

Address:

Phone: Fax:

Mobile:

E-mail:

Name:

Address:

Phone: Fax:

Mobile:

E-mail:

Name:

Address:

Phone: Fax:

Mobile:

E-mail:

U

Name:	Name:
Address:	Address:
Phone: Fax:	Phone: Fax:
Mobile:	Mobile:
E-mail:	E-mail:
Name:	Name:
Address:	Address:
Phone: Fax:	Phone: Fax:
Mobile:	Mobile:
E-mail:	E-mail:
Name:	Name:
Address:	Address:
Phone: Fax:	Phone: Fax:
Mobile:	Mobile:
E-mail:	E-mail:

Mouth of the Suir, Ireland *Watercolour, bodycolour on paper 31.6 x 44 cm* **Thomas Walmsley** *(1763-1806)*

U

Name:

Address:

Phone: Fax:

Mobile:

E-mail:

Name:

Address:

Phone: Fax:

Mobile:

E-mail:

Name:

Address:

Phone: Fax:

Mobile:

E-mail:

Name:

Address:

Phone: Fax:

Mobile:

E-mail:

Name:

Address:

Phone: Fax:

Mobile:

E-mail:

Name:

Address:

Phone: Fax:

Mobile:

E-mail:

Name:

Address:

Phone: Fax:

Mobile:

E-mail:

Name:

Address:

Phone: Fax:

Mobile:

E-mail:

Name:

Address:

Phone: Fax:

Mobile:

E-mail:

Name:

Address:

Phone: Fax:

Mobile:

E-mail:

Name:

Address:

Phone: Fax:

Mobile:

E-mail:

Name:

Address:

Phone: Fax:

Mobile:

E-mail:

V

Name:

Address:

Phone: Fax:

Mobile:

E-mail:

Name:

Address:

Phone: Fax:

Mobile:

E-mail:

Name:

Address:

Phone: Fax:

Mobile:

E-mail:

Name:

Address:

Phone: Fax:

Mobile:

E-mail:

Name:

Address:

Phone: Fax:

Mobile:

E-mail:

Name:

Address:

Phone: Fax:

Mobile:

E-mail:

Evening, Malahide, Co. Dublin (c. 1893) *Oil on prepared artist's canvas board 16.3 x 24 cm* **Margaret d'Arcy**

V

Name:

Address:

Phone: Fax:

Mobile:

E-mail:

Name:

Address:

Phone: Fax:

Mobile:

E-mail:

Name:

Address:

Phone: Fax:

Mobile:

E-mail:

Name:

Address:

Phone: Fax:

Mobile:

E-mail:

Name:

Address:

Phone: Fax:

Mobile:

E-mail:

Name:

Address:

Phone: Fax:

Mobile:

E-mail:

Name:

Address:

Phone: Fax:

Mobile:

E-mail:

Name:

Address:

Phone: Fax:

Mobile:

E-mail:

Name:

Address:

Phone: Fax:

Mobile:

E-mail:

Name:

Address:

Phone: Fax:

Mobile:

E-mail:

Name:

Address:

Phone: Fax:

Mobile:

E-mail:

Name:

Address:

Phone: Fax:

Mobile:

E-mail:

Name:

Address:

Phone: Fax:

Mobile:

E-mail:

Name:

Address:

Phone: Fax:

Mobile:

E-mail:

Name:

Address:

Phone: Fax:

Mobile:

E-mail:

Name:

Address:

Phone: Fax:

Mobile:

E-mail:

Name:

Address:

Phone: Fax:

Mobile:

E-mail:

Name:

Address:

Phone: Fax:

Mobile:

E-mail:

The Incoming Tide (c. 1937) *Oil on canvas on panel 35.1 x 46.4 cm* **Georgina Moutray Kyle** *(1865-1950)*

W

Name:

Address:

Phone: Fax:

Mobile:

E-mail:

Name:

Address:

Phone: Fax:

Mobile:

E-mail:

Name:

Address:

Phone: Fax:

Mobile:

E-mail:

Name:

Address:

Phone: Fax:

Mobile:

E-mail:

Name:

Address:

Phone: Fax:

Mobile:

E-mail:

Name:

Address:

Phone: Fax:

Mobile:

E-mail:

Name:

Address:

Phone: Fax:

Mobile:

E-mail:

Name:

Address:

Phone: Fax:

Mobile:

E-mail:

Name:

Address:

Phone: Fax:

Mobile:

E-mail:

Name:

Address:

Phone: Fax:

Mobile:

E-mail:

Name:

Address:

Phone: Fax:

Mobile:

E-mail:

Name:

Address:

Phone: Fax:

Mobile:

E-mail:

X

Name:	Name:
Address:	Address:
Phone: Fax:	Phone: Fax:
Mobile:	Mobile:
E-mail:	E-mail:
Name:	Name:
Address:	Address:
Phone: Fax:	Phone: Fax:
Mobile:	Mobile:
E-mail:	E-mail:
Name:	Name:
Address:	Address:
Phone: Fax:	Phone: Fax:
Mobile:	Mobile:
E-mail:	E-mail:

River Lagan, near Belfast *Oil on panel 18.2 x 25.3 cm* **William Gibbes MacKenzie** *(1857-1924)*

X

Name:

Address:

Phone: Fax:

Mobile:

E-mail:

Name:

Address:

Phone: Fax:

Mobile:

E-mail:

Name:

Address:

Phone: Fax:

Mobile:

E-mail:

Name:

Address:

Phone: Fax:

Mobile:

E-mail:

Name:

Address:

Phone: Fax:

Mobile:

E-mail:

Name:

Address:

Phone: Fax:

Mobile:

E-mail:

Name:

Address:

Phone: Fax:

Mobile:

E-mail:

Name:

Address:

Phone: Fax:

Mobile:

E-mail:

Name:

Address:

Phone: Fax:

Mobile:

E-mail:

Name:

Address:

Phone: Fax:

Mobile:

E-mail:

Name:

Address:

Phone: Fax:

Mobile:

E-mail:

Name:

Address:

Phone: Fax:

Mobile:

E-mail:

Y

Name:

Address:

Phone: Fax:

Mobile:

E-mail:

Name:

Address:

Phone: Fax:

Mobile:

E-mail:

Name:

Address:

Phone: Fax:

Mobile:

E-mail:

Name:

Address:

Phone: Fax:

Mobile:

E-mail:

Name:

Address:

Phone: Fax:

Mobile:

E-mail:

Name:

Address:

Phone: Fax:

Mobile:

E-mail:

Sailing Ships   *Watercolour, ink, pencil on paper 34.6 x 45.6 cm*   **Samuel Atkins** *(fl.1787-1808)*

Y

Name:

Address:

Phone: Fax:

Mobile:

E-mail:

Name:

Address:

Phone: Fax:

Mobile:

E-mail:

Name:

Address:

Phone: Fax:

Mobile:

E-mail:

Name:

Address:

Phone: Fax:

Mobile:

E-mail:

Name:

Address:

Phone: Fax:

Mobile:

E-mail:

Name:

Address:

Phone: Fax:

Mobile:

E-mail:

Y

Name:	Name:
Address:	Address:
Phone: Fax:	Phone: Fax:
Mobile:	Mobile:
E-mail:	E-mail:

Name:	Name:
Address:	Address:
Phone: Fax:	Phone: Fax:
Mobile:	Mobile:
E-mail:	E-mail:

Name:	Name:
Address:	Address:
Phone: Fax:	Phone: Fax:
Mobile:	Mobile:
E-mail:	E-mail:

Z

Name:

Address:

Phone: Fax:

Mobile:

E-mail:

Name:

Address:

Phone: Fax:

Mobile:

E-mail:

Name:

Address:

Phone: Fax:

Mobile:

E-mail:

Name:

Address:

Phone: Fax:

Mobile:

E-mail:

Name:

Address:

Phone: Fax:

Mobile:

E-mail:

Name:

Address:

Phone: Fax:

Mobile:

E-mail:

Emigrant Ship Leaving Belfast *(1852) Oil on canvas 71.4 x 91.3 cm* **James Glen Wilson** *(1827-1863)*

Z

Name:

Address:

Phone: Fax:

Mobile:

E-mail:

Name:

Address:

Phone: Fax:

Mobile:

E-mail:

Name:

Address:

Phone: Fax:

Mobile:

E-mail:

Name:

Address:

Phone: Fax:

Mobile:

E-mail:

Name:

Address:

Phone: Fax:

Mobile:

E-mail:

Name:

Address:

Phone: Fax:

Mobile:

E-mail:

Z

Name:
Address:

Phone: Fax:
Mobile:
E-mail:

Name:
Address:

Phone: Fax:
Mobile:
E-mail:

Name:
Address:

Phone: Fax:
Mobile:
E-mail:

Name:
Address:

Phone: Fax:
Mobile:
E-mail:

Name:
Address:

Phone: Fax:
Mobile:
E-mail:

Name:
Address:

Phone: Fax:
Mobile:
E-mail:

List of Illustrations

Acknowledgements

The publisher wishes to thank the following for permission to reproduce work in copyright:

The Ulster Museum

Text by Martyn Anglesea (Keeper of Fine Art, Ulster Museum) and Paul Harron

The publisher wishes to thank Pat McLean, Rights and Reproductions Officer, Ulster Museum for her help in compiling this collection.